Masterpieces

Multiplication and Division

YEARS 3 AND 4

Contents

Multiplication and division facts   4

Mental calculation strategies   17

Pencil-and-paper procedures   30

Checking results   43

Answers   59

Contents

Worksheet title	Ability group	Pages
Multiplication and division facts		
Diagnostic assessment: × and ÷ facts		4
• recall of tables facts	A B C	5–7
• halves of multiples of 5 to 100	A	8
• halves of multiples of 10 to 500	B	9
• halves of multiples of 100 to 5000	C	10
• halves and doubles of numbers to 20	A	11
• doubles of numbers to 50	B C	12–13
• doubles of multiples of 5 to 100	A	14
• doubles of multiples of 10 to 500	B	15
• doubles of multiples of 100 to 5000	C	16
Mental calculation strategies		
Diagnostic assessment: mental calculation strategies		17
• doubling and halving known facts	A B C	18–20
• using closely related facts	A B C	21–3
• partitioning when multiplying	A B C	24–6
• multiplying and dividing by 10	A	27
• multiplying and dividing by 100	B	28
• multiplying and dividing by 1000	C	29
Pencil-and-paper procedures		
Diagnostic assessment: pencil-and-paper procedures		30
• approximating	A B C	31–3
• TU × U	A B	34–5
• HTU × U	C	36
• TU ÷ U	A B C	37–9
• remainders as whole numbers	A	40
• rounding remainders up or down	B	41
• remainders as decimals	C	42
Checking results		
Diagnostic assessment: checking results		43
• checking with the inverse operation	A B C	44–6
• repeating multiplication in a different order	A B C	47–9
• checking by approximating (rounding to 10)	A	50
• checking by approximating (rounding to 10, 100)	B C	51–2
• checking with an equivalent calculation	A B C	53–5
• using tests of divisibility by 10, 100	A	56
• using tests of divisibility by 2, 5	B	57
• using tests of divisibility by 3, 4	C	58

Coverage of National Numeracy Strategy "Framework"

Year 3 Objectives	Year 4 Objectives
Rapid recall of × and ÷ facts	
• multiplication facts for the 2, 5 and 10 times tables • begin to know the 3 and 4 times tables • division facts corresponding to the 2, 5 and 10 times tables • doubles of all whole numbers to at least 20 • doubles of multiples of 5 to 100 • doubles of multiples of 50 to 500 and all the corresponding halves	• multiplication facts for the 2, 3, 4, 5 and 10 times tables • begin to know multiplication facts for the 6, 7, 8 and 9 times tables • division facts corresponding to the 2, 3, 4, 5 and 10 times tables • doubles of all whole numbers to 50 • doubles of multiples of 10 to 500 • doubles of multiples of 100 to 5000 • and all the corresponding halves
Mental calculation strategies (× and ÷)	
• to multiply by 10, 100, shift the digits one/two places to the left • use doubling or halving, starting from known facts • say or write a division statement corresponding to a given multiplication statement • use known number facts and place value to carry out mentally simple multiplications and divisions	• use doubling or halving, starting from known facts • use closely related facts • partition • use the relationship between multiplication and division • use known number facts and place value to multiply and divide integers, including by 10 and then 100 (whole-number answers)
Pencil-and-paper procedures	
	• approximate first • use informal pencil-and-paper methods to support, record or explain multiplications and divisions • develop and refine written methods for TU × U, TU ÷ U
Checking results	
• check halving with doubling and division with multiplication • repeat with an equivalent calculation • check with an equivalent calculation	• check with the inverse operation • check with an equivalent calculation • estimate and check by approximating (round to nearest 10 or 100)

Name _____   Date _____

Diagnostic assessment

1 Write the answers in the boxes.

$2 \times 2 =$ ☐ $2 \times 6 =$ ☐ $5 \times 5 =$ ☐

$5 \times 8 =$ ☐ $10 \times 5 =$ ☐ $10 \times 10 =$ ☐

2 Double each of these numbers.

7 ☐   15 ☐   18 ☐

Find half of each of these numbers.

12 ☐   16 ☐   20 ☐

A
Sheets

3 Write the answers in the boxes.

$3 \times 3 =$ ☐ $3 \times 8 =$ ☐ $3 \times 9 =$ ☐

$4 \times 4 =$ ☐ $4 \times 6 =$ ☐ $4 \times 8 =$ ☐

4 Double each of these numbers.

16 ☐   24 ☐   31 ☐

Find half of each of these numbers.

14 ☐   24 ☐   42 ☐

B
Sheets

5 Write the answers in the boxes.

$6 \times 6 =$ ☐ $7 \times 6 =$ ☐ $7 \times 7 =$ ☐

$8 \times 8 =$ ☐ $8 \times 9 =$ ☐ $9 \times 9 =$ ☐

6 Double each of these numbers.

21 ☐   28 ☐   37 ☐

Find half of each of these numbers.

18 ☐   42 ☐   78 ☐

C
Sheets

| *Masterpieces:* **Multiplication and Division** MULTIPLICATION AND DIVISION FACTS   **YEARS 3/4**

Name _____ Date _____

Recall of facts for the 2, 5 and 10 times tables

1 Can you join up these numbers in the right order? Start at 0.

2 times table

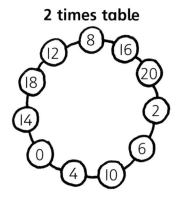

5 times table

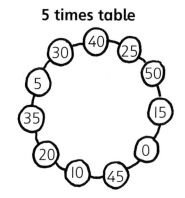

2 Colour the squares with numbers in the **2 times** table. What letter do you make?

29	18	9	14	25
7	6	3	4	17
13	12	8	16	19
1	20	5	2	11
15	0	23	10	27

3 Colour the squares with numbers in the **5 times** table. What letter do you make?

20	16	8	36	45
18	5	4	25	31
12	9	0	42	27
22	15	17	10	2
35	24	21	48	30

4 Do these quickly.

50 ÷ 10 = ☐   10 ÷ 2 = ☐   40 ÷ 10 = ☐   20 ÷ 5 = ☐

30 ÷ 10 = ☐   18 ÷ 2 = ☐   40 ÷ 5 = ☐   50 ÷ 5 = ☐

28 ÷ 2 = ☐   100 ÷ 10 = ☐   60 ÷ 10 = ☐   12 ÷ 2 = ☐

Name _____ Date _____

Recall of facts for the 3 and 4 times tables

1 Match the questions to the correct answers.

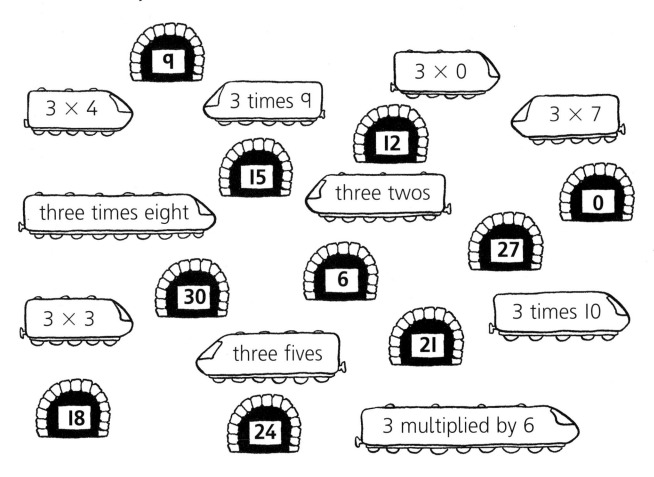

2 Write as many **4 times** tables facts as you can.
Put one at the end of each line. Draw more lines if you need to.

$4 \times 5 = 20$

4×

3 Do these quickly.

$20 \div 4 = \boxed{}$ $24 \div 4 = \boxed{}$ $30 \div 3 = \boxed{}$ $18 \div 3 = \boxed{}$

$21 \div 3 = \boxed{}$ $27 \div 3 = \boxed{}$ $32 \div 4 = \boxed{}$ $36 \div 4 = \boxed{}$

B *Masterpieces:* **Multiplication and Division** MULTIPLICATION AND DIVISION FACTS   **YEARS 3/4**

Recall of facts for the 6, 7, 8 and 9 times tables

1 Colour the squares with numbers in the **6 times** table. What letter do you make?

21	18	42	60	25
7	6	3	4	17
13	12	36	24	19
1	30	5	2	11
15	48	23	10	27

2 Colour the squares with numbers in the **8 times** table. What letter do you make?

22	16	8	36	44
18	72	4	24	31
54	48	12	40	27
34	64	20	32	2
35	80	56	47	30

3 Do these quickly.

$9 \times 2 = \boxed{}$ $7 \times 7 = \boxed{}$ $9 \times 5 = \boxed{}$ $7 \times 6 = \boxed{}$

$9 \times 0 = \boxed{}$ $35 \div 7 = \boxed{}$ $72 \div 9 = \boxed{}$ $49 \div 7 = \boxed{}$

$54 \div 6 = \boxed{}$ $56 \div 8 = \boxed{}$ $9 \times 9 = \boxed{}$ $7 \times 0 = \boxed{}$

$9 \times 8 = \boxed{}$ $63 \div 9 = \boxed{}$ $48 \div 6 = \boxed{}$ $36 \div 4 = \boxed{}$

4 Write some different ways of multiplying or dividing to get the answer 24.

12×2

$2 \times 2 \times 6$

$96 \div 4$

Name _____ Date _____

Halves of multiples of 5 to 100

1 Write half of these numbers.

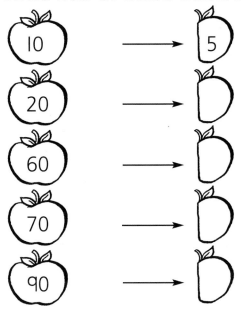
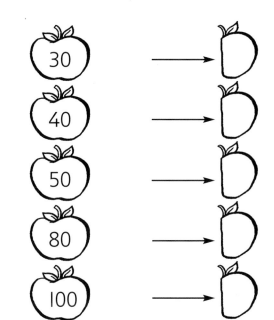

2 Join each balloon to the person holding half that number.

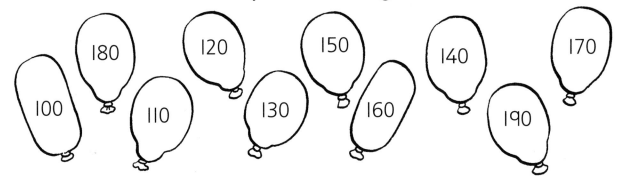

A *Masterpieces:* **Multiplication and Division** MULTIPLICATION AND DIVISION FACTS **YEARS 3/4**

Name _____ Date _____

Halves of multiples of 10 to 500

1 Write half of these numbers.

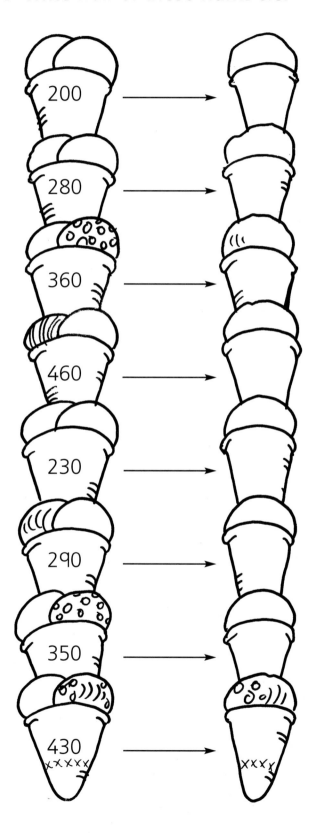

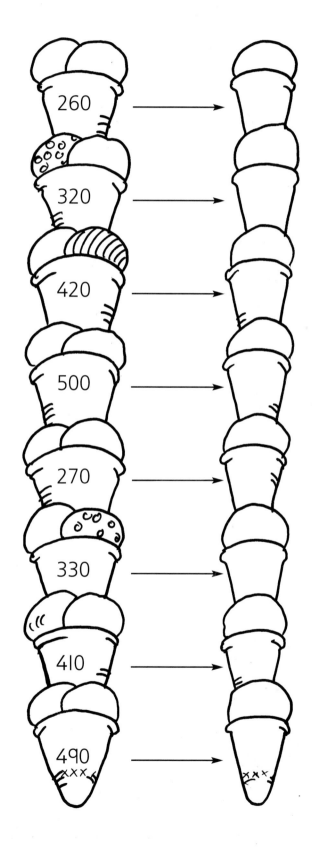

Name _____ Date _____

Halves of multiples of 100 to 5000

1 In each space write half of the number in the aeroplane.

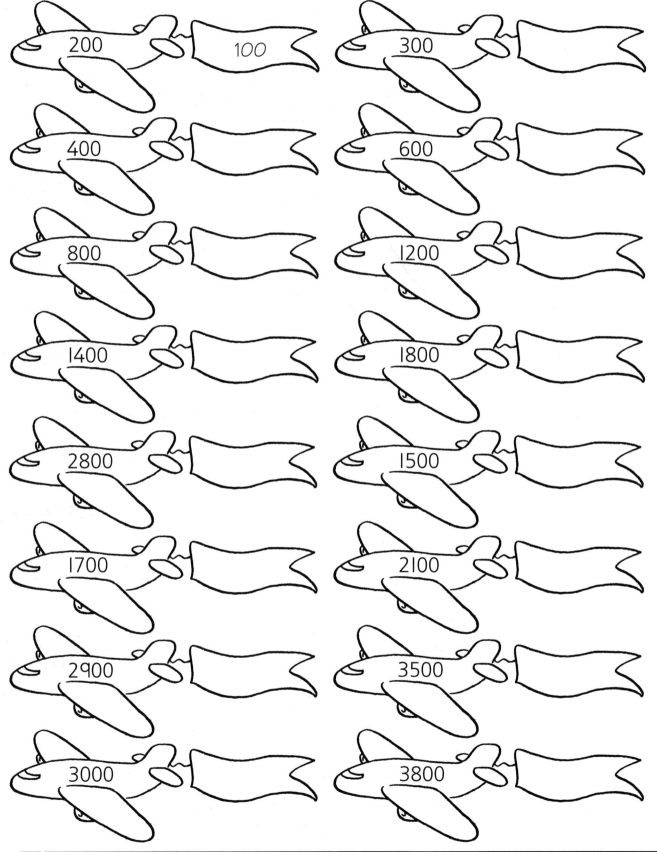

200 100

300

400

600

800

1200

1400

1800

2800

1500

1700

2100

2900

3500

3000

3800

C *Masterpieces:* **Multiplication and Division** MULTIPLICATION AND DIVISION FACTS **YEARS 3/4**

Name _____ Date _____

Halves and doubles of numbers to 20

1 Draw a line from each paint pot to the ladder and colour in the answer.

Double 2

Half of 10

Half of 18

$\frac{1}{2}$ of 14

Twice 13

Double 12

Double 14

Twice 11

Double 16

Double 18

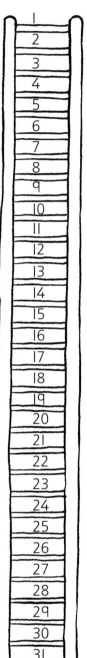
Ladder numbers: 1, 2, 3, 4, 5, 6, 7, 8, 9, 10, 11, 12, 13, 14, 15, 16, 17, 18, 19, 20, 21, 22, 23, 24, 25, 26, 27, 28, 29, 30, 31, 32, 33, 34, 35, 36, 37, 38, 39, 40, 41

$\frac{1}{2}$ of 12

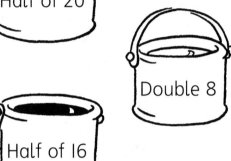
Half of 20

Double 8

Half of 16

Double 9

Twice 10

Twice 15

Double 19

Twice 17

Double 20

Name _____ Date _____

Doubles of numbers to 50

Work out the doubles of these numbers like this:

1   Double 24 ⟶ 24 + 24 ⟶ (20 + 4) + (20 + 4) ⟶ 40 + 8 ⟶ 48

Twice 32

Double 23

Twice 34

Double 25

Twice 38

Double 4I

Twice 26

Double 33

2 Find half of these numbers.

16		24		36		38		44	
40		50		56		64		76	

B *Masterpieces:* **Multiplication and Division** MULTIPLICATION AND DIVISION FACTS   **YEARS 3/4**

Name _____ Date _____

More doubles of numbers to 50

Work out the doubles of these numbers like this:

1   Double 37 ⟶ 37 + 37 ⟶ (30 + 7) + (30 + 7) ⟶ 60 + 14 ⟶ 74

Twice 26

Double 39

Twice 43

Double 45

Twice 47

Double 49

Twice 38

Double 29

2 Halve these numbers.

24		34		36		42		38	
46		50		68		76		84	

Doubles of multiples of 5 to 100

1 Write the doubles of each of these numbers.

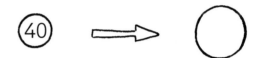

2 Join the circles with their doubles.

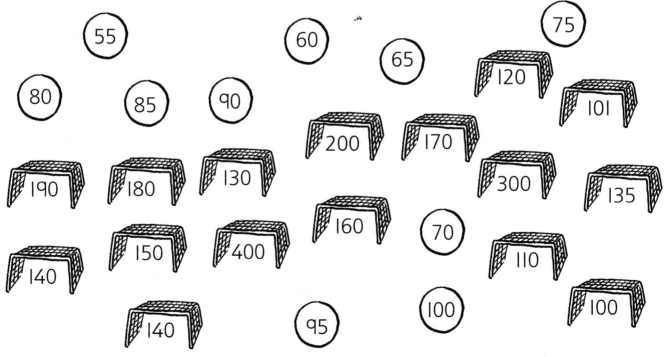

Name ______________________ Date ____________

Doubles of multiples of 10 to 500

1 Start at the bottom of the page.
Join the number in each cloud to its double in the tower.

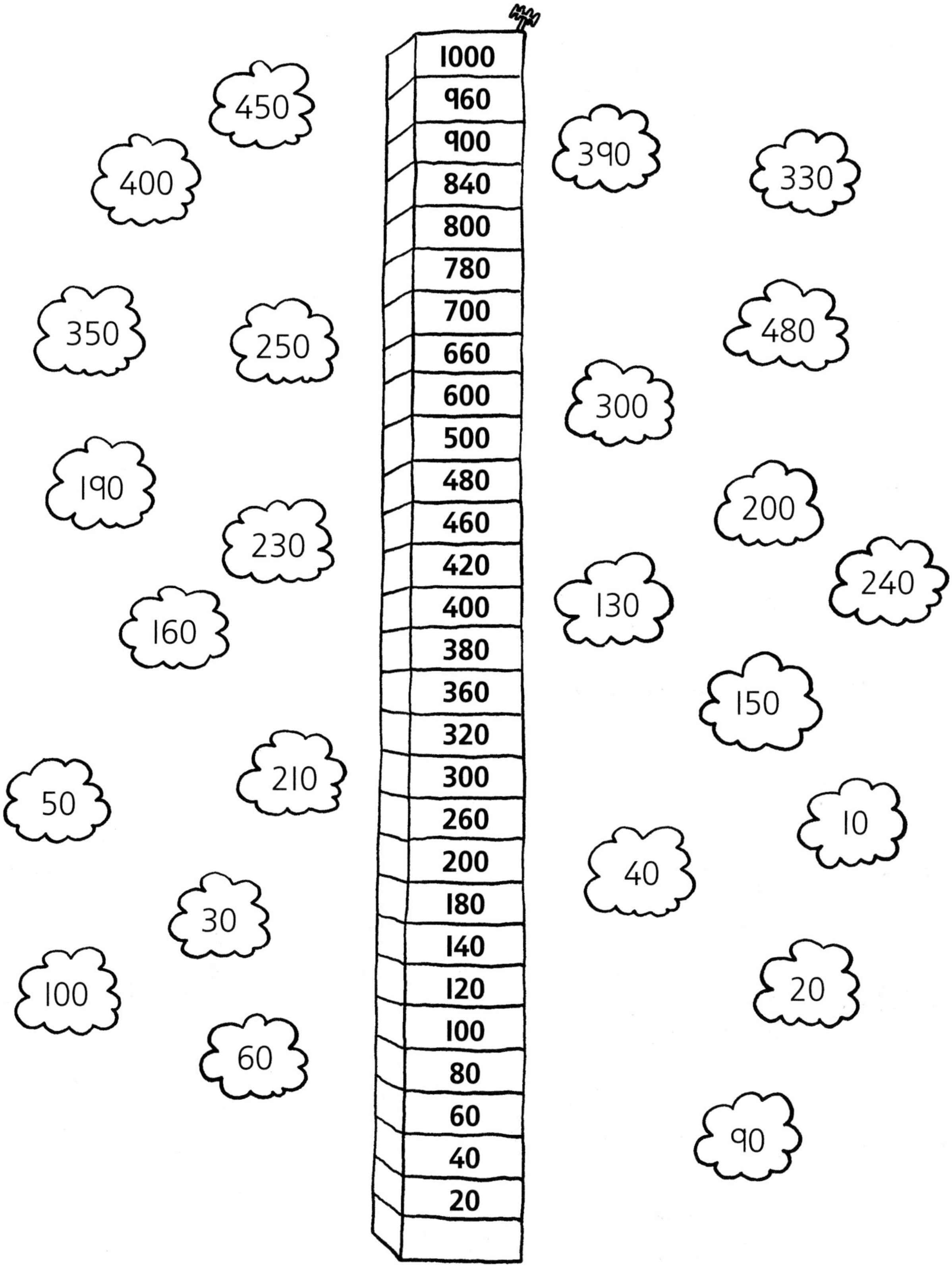

450
400
350
250
190
230
160
50
210
30
100
60
1000
960
900
840
800
780
700
660
600
500
480
460
420
400
380
360
320
300
260
200
180
140
120
100
80
60
40
20
390
330
480
300
200
240
130
150
10
40
20
90

Doubles of multiples of 100 to 5000

1 Start at the bottom of the page.
   Join the numbers in the letters to their doubles in the postbox.

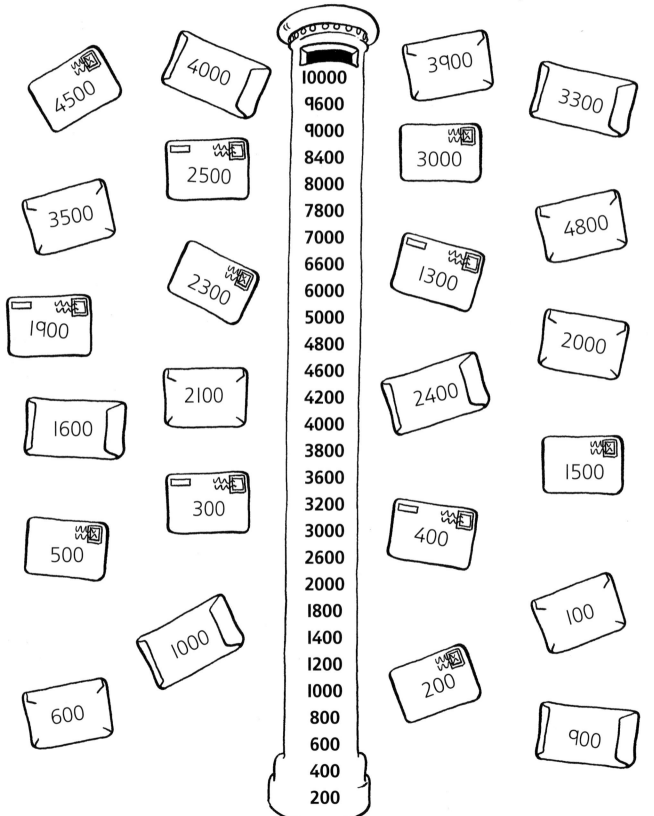

Name _____ Date _____

Diagnostic assessment

1 Write the missing numbers.

10×2	halve	5×2
20	→	

5×6	double	10×6
30	→	

A Sheets

2 $11 \times 12 = \boxed{}$ $11 \times 14 = \boxed{}$ $11 \times 25 = \boxed{}$

3 $10 \times 23 = \boxed{}$ $160 \div 10 = \boxed{}$ $340 \div 10 = \boxed{}$

4 Write the missing numbers.

4×6	halve	2×6
24	→	

2×7	double	4×7
14	→	

B Sheets

5 $9 \times 12 = \boxed{}$ $9 \times 15 = \boxed{}$ $9 \times 27 = \boxed{}$

6 $100 \times 31 = \boxed{}$ $800 \div 10 = \boxed{}$ $1300 \div 100 = \boxed{}$

7 Write the missing numbers.

$4 \times 30 = 120$ so $8 \times 30 = \boxed{}$ $3 \times 40 = 120$ so $6 \times 40 = \boxed{}$

$8 \times 12 = 96$ so $4 \times 12 = \boxed{}$ $6 \times 30 = 180$ so $3 \times 30 = \boxed{}$

C Sheets

8 $11 \times 13 = \boxed{}$ $9 \times 14 = \boxed{}$ $6 \times 25 = \boxed{}$

9 $1000 \times 26 = \boxed{}$ $8000 \div 1000 = \boxed{}$

Name _____ Date _____

Doubling and halving known facts

1 Fill in the **5 times** and **10 times** snakes.

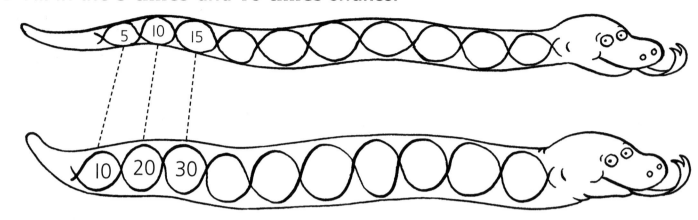

Look at the numbers in the two snakes. What do you notice?

....

....

2

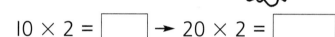

Use doubles to help you answer these.

10 × 4 = ☐ → 20 × 4 = ☐

2 × 3 = ☐ → 4 × 3 = ☐   10 × 2 = ☐ → 20 × 2 = ☐

2 × 6 = ☐ → 4 × 6 = ☐   10 × 5 = ☐ → 20 × 5 = ☐

2 × 8 = ☐ → 4 × 8 = ☐   10 × 7 = ☐ → 20 × 7 = ☐

3

Use halves to help you answer these.

10 × 3 = ☐ → 5 × 3 = ☐

10 × 4 = ☐ → 5 × 4 = ☐   10 × 5 = ☐ → 5 × 5 = ☐

10 × 6 = ☐ → 5 × 6 = ☐   10 × 7 = ☐ → 5 × 7 = ☐

10 × 8 = ☐ → 5 × 8 = ☐   10 × 9 = ☐ → 5 × 9 = ☐

Name _____ Date _____

Doubling and halving known facts

1

$3 \times 7 =$ ☐ → $6 \times 7 =$ ☐

Use doubles to help you answer these.

$2 \times 9 =$ ☐ → $4 \times 9 =$ ☐ $3 \times 9 =$ ☐ → $6 \times 9 =$ ☐

$3 \times 6 =$ ☐ → $6 \times 6 =$ ☐ $4 \times 7 =$ ☐ → $8 \times 7 =$ ☐

$4 \times 8 =$ ☐ → $8 \times 8 =$ ☐ $10 \times 9 =$ ☐ → $20 \times 9 =$ ☐

2 $2 \times 20 =$ ☐ **so** $4 \times 20 =$ ☐ $2 \times 30 =$ ☐ **so** $4 \times 30 =$ ☐

$3 \times 12 =$ ☐ **so** $6 \times 12 =$ ☐ $4 \times 25 =$ ☐ **so** $8 \times 25 =$ ☐

$3 \times 20 =$ ☐ **so** $6 \times 20 =$ ☐ $4 \times 40 =$ ☐ **so** $4 \times 80 =$ ☐

3

Use halves to help you answer these.

$10 \times 3 =$ ☐ → $5 \times 3 =$ ☐

$10 \times 4 =$ ☐ → $5 \times 4 =$ ☐ $10 \times 5 =$ ☐ → $5 \times 5 =$ ☐

$10 \times 6 =$ ☐ → $5 \times 6 =$ ☐ $10 \times 7 =$ ☐ → $5 \times 7 =$ ☐

$10 \times 8 =$ ☐ → $5 \times 8 =$ ☐ $10 \times 9 =$ ☐ → $5 \times 9 =$ ☐

4 $10 \times 30 =$ ☐ **so** $5 \times 30 =$ ☐ $4 \times 40 =$ ☐ **so** $2 \times 40 =$ ☐

$8 \times 15 =$ ☐ **so** $4 \times 15 =$ ☐ $6 \times 25 =$ ☐ **so** $3 \times 25 =$ ☐

Name _____ Date _____

Doubling and halving known facts

1

Use doubles to help you answer these.

$4 \times 20 =$ | 80 | so $8 \times 20 =$ | ☐

$3 \times 30 =$ ☐ so $6 \times 30 =$ ☐ $3 \times 40 =$ ☐ so $6 \times 40 =$ ☐

$6 \times 12 =$ ☐ so $12 \times 12 =$ ☐ $4 \times 60 =$ ☐ so $8 \times 60 =$ ☐

$8 \times 9 =$ ☐ so $16 \times 9 =$ ☐ $6 \times 30 =$ ☐ so $12 \times 30 =$ ☐

2

Use halves to help you answer these.

$10 \times 30 =$ | 300 | so $5 \times 30 =$ ☐

$10 \times 50 =$ ☐ so $5 \times 50 =$ ☐ $10 \times 40 =$ ☐ so $5 \times 40 =$ ☐

$10 \times 17 =$ ☐ so $5 \times 17 =$ ☐ $10 \times 25 =$ ☐ so $5 \times 25 =$ ☐

$10 \times 36 =$ ☐ so $5 \times 36 =$ ☐ $10 \times 42 =$ ☐ so $5 \times 42 =$ ☐

3 Use doubles to finish these patterns.

$1 \times 25 =$ | 25 | $1 \times 30 =$ | 30 | $1 \times 35 =$ | 35 |

$2 \times 25 =$ ☐ $2 \times 30 =$ ☐ $2 \times 35 =$ ☐

$4 \times 25 =$ ☐ $4 \times 30 =$ ☐ $4 \times 35 =$ ☐

$8 \times 25 =$ ☐ $8 \times 30 =$ ☐ $8 \times 35 =$ ☐

$16 \times 25 =$ ☐ $16 \times 30 =$ ☐ $16 \times 35 =$ ☐

$32 \times 25 =$ ☐ $32 \times 30 =$ ☐ $32 \times 35 =$ ☐

Name _____ **Date** _____

Using closely related facts

It's easy to multiply by 11. Look:

$11 \times 12 = (10 \times 12) + (1 \times 12) = 120 + 12 = 132$

1 Do these in the same way.

$11 \times 15 = (\boxed{} \times 15) + (\boxed{} \times 15) = \boxed{} + \boxed{} = \boxed{}$

$11 \times 16 = (\boxed{} \times 16) + (\boxed{} \times 16) = \boxed{} + \boxed{} = \boxed{}$

$11 \times 20 = (\boxed{} \times 20) + (\boxed{} \times 20) = \boxed{} + \boxed{} = \boxed{}$

$11 \times 25 = (\boxed{} \times 25) + (\boxed{} \times 25) = \boxed{} + \boxed{} = \boxed{}$

$11 \times 30 = (\boxed{} \times 30) + (\boxed{} \times 30) = \boxed{} + \boxed{} = \boxed{}$

2 Do these in the same way.

$11 \times 17 = \boxed{}$ $11 \times 21 = \boxed{}$ $11 \times 24 = \boxed{}$

11 boxes of 19 sweets =  sweets

11 sets of 36 pencils =  pencils

11 bags of 40 coins =  coins

11 tanks of 45 fish =  fish

Name _____ Date _____

Using closely related facts

It's easy to multiply by 9. Look:

$$9 \times 12 = (10 \times 12) - (1 \times 12) = 120 - 12 = 108$$

1 Do these in the same way.

$9 \times 17 = (\boxed{} \times 17) - (\boxed{} \times 17) = \boxed{} - \boxed{} = \boxed{}$

$9 \times 26 = (\boxed{} \times 26) - (\boxed{} \times 26) = \boxed{} - \boxed{} = \boxed{}$

$9 \times 30 = (\boxed{} \times 30) - (\boxed{} \times 30) = \boxed{} - \boxed{} = \boxed{}$

$9 \times 35 = (\boxed{} \times 35) - (\boxed{} \times 35) = \boxed{} - \boxed{} = \boxed{}$

2 Write the answers in the spaces.

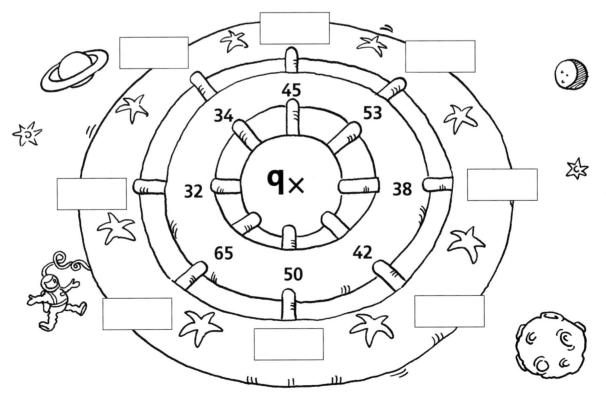

3 Choose your own numbers to multiply by 9.

Name _____ Date _____

Using closely related facts

1

It's easy to multiply by 6 if you know your 2× and 4× tables. Here's a trick.

$$6 × 3 = (2 × 3) + (4 × 3) = 18$$

Use the 2× and the 4× tables to do these.

6 × 4 = ☐   6 × 5 = ☐   6 × 6 = ☐   6 × 7 = ☐

6 × 8 = ☐   6 × 9 = ☐   6 × 11 = ☐   6 × 12 = ☐

2 To multiply by 9 we can use the 3× and 6× tables.

$$9 × 5 = (3 × 5) + (6 × 5) = 45$$

Use the 3× and the 6× tables to do these.

9 × 4 = ☐   9 × 5 = ☐   9 × 6 = ☐   9 × 7 = ☐

9 × 8 = ☐   9 × 9 = ☐   9 × 11 = ☐   9 × 12 = ☐

3 What tables facts can you add to make those in the rabbits?
Do as many as you can.

$(2 × 5) + (2 × 5) + (2 × 5)$

6 × 5

8 × 9

7 × 8

Name _____ Date _____

Partitioning when multiplying

1 ⟮ Do these questions by 'splitting up'. ⟯

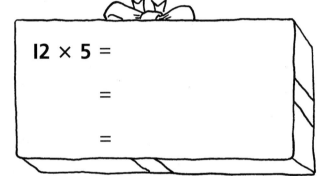

$13 \times 2 = (10 \times 2) + (3 \times 2)$

$= 20 + 6$

$= 26$

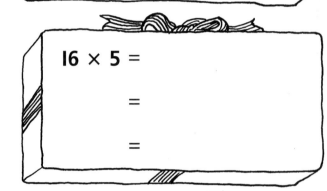

$15 \times 2 = (\quad) + (\quad)$

$= \quad + $

$=$

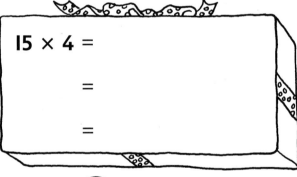

$12 \times 5 =$

$=$

$=$

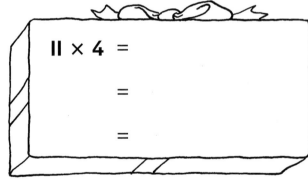

$16 \times 5 =$

$=$

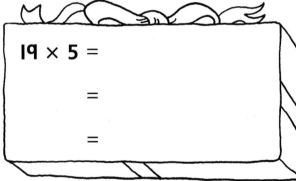

$15 \times 4 =$

$=$

$=$

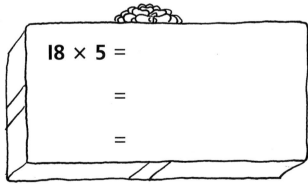

$11 \times 4 =$

$=$

$=$

$19 \times 5 =$

$=$

$=$

$18 \times 5 =$

$=$

$=$

2 Make up some of your own and work them out in the same way.

Name _____ Date _____

Partitioning when multiplying

1

Do these questions by 'splitting up'.

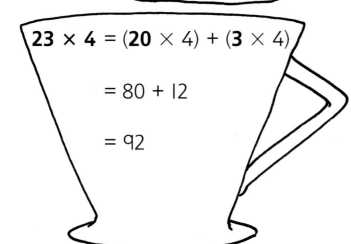

$23 \times 4 = (20 \times 4) + (3 \times 4)$

$= 80 + 12$

$= 92$

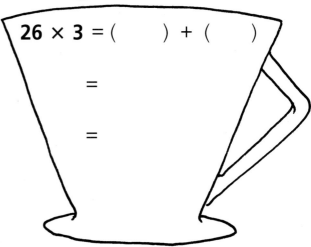

$26 \times 3 = ($ $) + ($ $)$

$=$

$=$

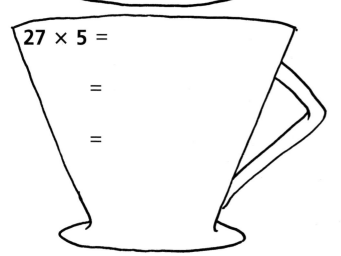

$27 \times 5 =$

$=$

$=$

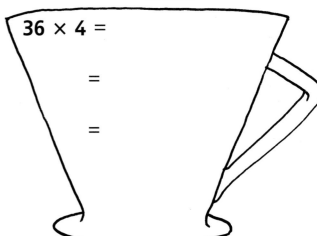

$36 \times 4 =$

$=$

$=$

2 Do these in the same way.

$$38 \times 5$$

$(\boxed{} \times \boxed{}) + (\boxed{} \times \boxed{})$

$= \boxed{} + \boxed{} = \boxed{}$

$$43 \times 4$$

$(\boxed{} \times \boxed{}) + (\boxed{} \times \boxed{})$

$= \boxed{} + \boxed{} = \boxed{}$

$$54 \times 5$$

$(\boxed{} \times \boxed{}) + (\boxed{} \times \boxed{})$

$= \boxed{} + \boxed{} = \boxed{}$

$$67 \times 3$$

$(\boxed{} \times \boxed{}) + (\boxed{} \times \boxed{})$

$= \boxed{} + \boxed{} = \boxed{}$

Partitioning when multiplying

1

You can 'split up' numbers to help multiply them.

123 × 4 is the same as (**100** × 4) + (**20** × 4) + (**3** × 4)

123 × 3 = ([ ] × 3) + ([ ] × 3) + ([ ] × 3)

134 × 3 = ([ ] × 3) + ([ ] × 3) + ([ ] × 3)

145 × 4 = ([ ] × 4) + ([ ] × 4) + ([ ] × 4)

156 × 6 = ([ ] × 6) + ([ ] × 6) + ([ ] × 6)

130 × 6 = ([ ] × 6) + ([ ] × 6) + ([ ] × 6)

103 × 7 = ([ ] × 7) + ([ ] × 7) + ([ ] × 7)

181 × 8 = ([ ] × 8) + ([ ] × 8) + ([ ] × 8)

2 Choose your own numbers for these.

= [ ] × [ ] + [ ] × [ ] + [ ] × [ ]

= [ ] × [ ] + [ ] × [ ] + [ ] × [ ]

= [ ] × [ ] + [ ] × [ ] + [ ] × [ ]

C *Masterpieces:* **Multiplication and Division** MENTAL CALCULATION STRATEGIES **YEARS 3/4**

Multiplying and dividing by 10

1 Write the numbers coming out of the machines.

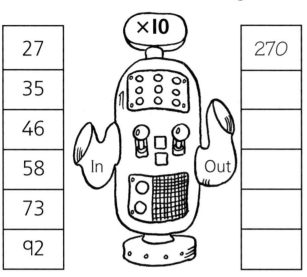

	×10	
27		270
35		
46		
58		
73		
92		

	÷10	
240		
320		
400		
530		
850		
970		

2 Write the numbers going into the machines.

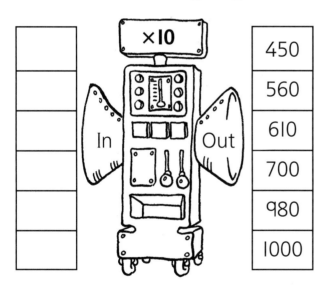

	×10	
		450
		560
		610
		700
		980
		1000

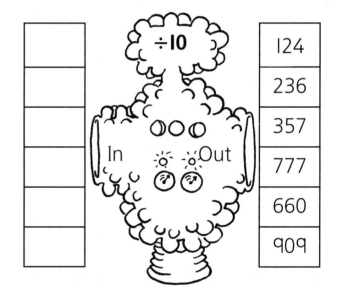

	÷10	
		124
		236
		357
		777
		660
		909

3 Draw a ×10 or a ÷10 machine of your own and write numbers going in and coming out.

Name _____ Date _____

Multiplying and dividing by 100

1 Multiply each number by 100 and write the answer underneath.

Tth	Th	H	T	U	
				6	×100
			3	2	×100
			5	8	×100
			6	4	×100
		1	9	8	×100

2 Divide each number by 100 and write the answer underneath.

Tth	Th	H	T	U	
		6	0	0	÷100
		9	0	0	÷100
	1	2	0	0	÷100
	2	3	0	0	÷100
3	6	0	0	0	÷100

3 Write the missing numbers.

×100

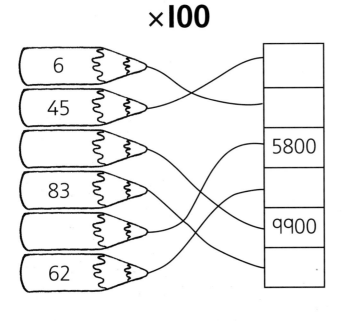

÷100

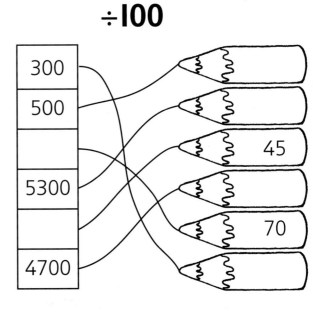

Name _____ Date _____

Multiplying and dividing by 1000

1 Multiply each number by 1000 and write the answer underneath.

Tth	Th	H	T	U	
				7	×1000
			6	2	×1000
			9	8	×1000
			6	4	×1000

2 Divide each number by 1000 and write the answer underneath.

Tth	Th	H	T	U	
	4	0	0	0	÷1000
	8	0	0	0	÷1000
4	1	0	0	0	÷1000
6	7	0	0	0	÷1000

3
$4 \times 1000 =$ ☐

$1000 \times 38 =$ ☐

$6000 \div 1000 =$ ☐

$15000 \div 1000 =$ ☐

$23 \times 1000 =$ ☐

$1000 \times 72 =$ ☐

$8000 \div 1000 =$ ☐

$36000 \div 1000 =$ ☐

4 Write your answers to these questions in numbers.

one thousand times thirty one ☐

eleven times one thousand ☐

one thousand multiplied by sixty-six ☐

forty multiplied by one thousand ☐

Name _____ Date _____

Diagnostic assessment

1 Round each of these numbers to the nearest 10.

19 ☐   32 ☐   46 ☐   75 ☐

2 Write the answers in the boxes.

$23 \times 2 =$ ☐ $21 \times 5 =$ ☐ $22 \times 4 =$ ☐

$16 \div 2 =$ ☐ $20 \div 4 =$ ☐ $36 \div 5 =$ ☐

A Sheets

3 Round each of these numbers to the nearest 10.

37 ☐   52 ☐   86 ☐   95 ☐

4 Round each of these numbers to the nearest 100.

270 ☐   525 ☐   382 ☐   650 ☐

5 Write the answers in the boxes.

$34 \times 3 =$ ☐ $43 \times 4 =$ ☐ $36 \times 5 =$ ☐

$21 \div 3 =$ ☐ $38 \div 4 =$ ☐ $45 \div 6 =$ ☐

B Sheets

6 Round each of these numbers to the nearest 10 and 100.

117   nearest 10 → ☐   nearest 100 → ☐

356   nearest 10 → ☐   nearest 100 → ☐

7 Write the answers in the boxes.

$134 \times 2 =$ ☐ $143 \times 4 =$ ☐ $346 \times 5 =$ ☐

$72 \div 9 =$ ☐ $68 \div 8 =$ ☐ $57 \div 6 =$ ☐

C Sheets

Name _____ Date _____

Approximating

1 Round these numbers to the nearest 10.

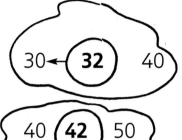
30 ← **32** 40

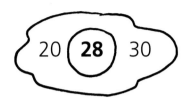
20 **28** 30

30 **37** 40

40 **42** 50

30 **38** 40

50 **54** 60

60 **65** 70

70 **78** 80

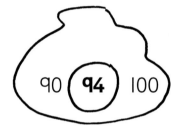
90 **94** 100

90 **99** 100

2 Round each of these numbers to the nearest 10.

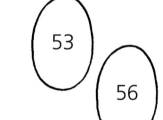 53

56

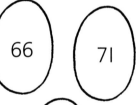 66   71

58

93

119

55

 94

 89

106

101

 **60**

70

 **50**

80

 **90**

100

110

120

Masterpieces: Ginn & Company 1999. Copying permitted for purchasing school only. This material is not copyright free.

Approximating

> To get an **approximate** answer we can **round** numbers to the nearest 10 or 100.

1

Round to nearest 10

$19 \times 2 \longrightarrow \boxed{20} \times 2 = 40$

Round to nearest 10

$28 \times 5 \longrightarrow \boxed{} \times 5 = \boxed{}$

$37 \times 3 \longrightarrow \boxed{} \times 3 = \boxed{}$

$17 \times 5 \longrightarrow \boxed{} \times 5 = \boxed{}$

$21 \times 5 \longrightarrow \boxed{} \times 5 = \boxed{}$

$18 \times 2 \longrightarrow \boxed{} \times 2 = \boxed{}$

$22 \times 2 \longrightarrow \boxed{} \times 2 = \boxed{}$

$29 \times 2 \longrightarrow \boxed{} \times 2 = \boxed{}$

$33 \times 3 \longrightarrow \boxed{} \times 3 = \boxed{}$

Round to nearest 100

$211 \times 5 \longrightarrow \boxed{} \times 5 = \boxed{}$

$322 \times 2 \longrightarrow \boxed{} \times 2 = \boxed{}$

$289 \times 5 \longrightarrow \boxed{} \times 5 = \boxed{}$

$429 \times 2 \longrightarrow \boxed{} \times 2 = \boxed{}$

$393 \times 3 \longrightarrow \boxed{} \times 3 = \boxed{}$

$541 \times 4 \longrightarrow \boxed{} \times 4 = \boxed{}$

$582 \times 3 \longrightarrow \boxed{} \times 3 = \boxed{}$

$614 \times 2 \longrightarrow \boxed{} \times 2 = \boxed{}$

2 Write down some numbers between 0 and 1000 and round them to the nearest 10 to 100.

Name _____ Date _____

Approximating

1 Write in the spaces like the one shown.

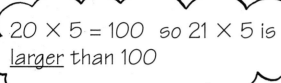

$20 \times 5 = 100$ so 21×5 is _larger_ than 100

21 × 5

32 × 6

118 × 4

292 × 7

319 × 8

597 × 9

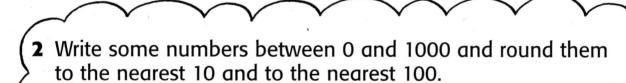

2 Write some numbers between 0 and 1000 and round them to the nearest 10 and to the nearest 100.

Name _____ Date _____

TU × U: no exchange

1 Work out the answers to these questions. Approximate first.

$$24 \times 2 \xrightarrow{\text{about } 40} 2 \begin{array}{|c|c|} \hline \overset{20}{40} & \overset{4}{8} \\ \hline \end{array} = 48$$

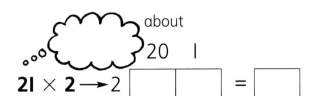

$21 \times 2 \rightarrow 2$ [20 | 1] = [ ]   about

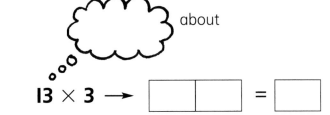

$23 \times 2 \rightarrow$ [|] = [ ]   about

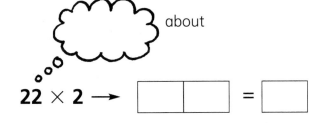

$22 \times 2 \rightarrow$ [|] = [ ]   about

$13 \times 3 \rightarrow$ [|] = [ ]   about

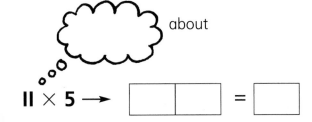

$11 \times 5 \rightarrow$ [|] = [ ]   about

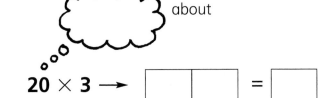

$20 \times 3 \rightarrow$ [|] = [ ]   about

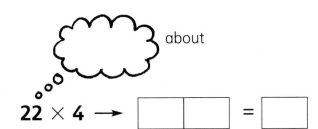

$22 \times 4 \rightarrow$ [|] = [ ]   about

$23 \times 3 \rightarrow$ [|] = [ ]   about

2 Write 4 questions of your own and do them in the same way.

TU × U: with exchange

The number at the top shows your score.
Write what your new score would be if you landed in each space.

1

2

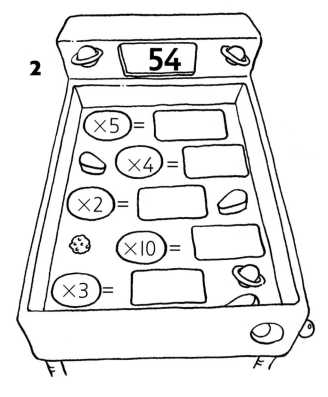

3

4

Name _____ Date _____

HTU × U: with exchange

1 Work out the answers to these questions. Approximate first.

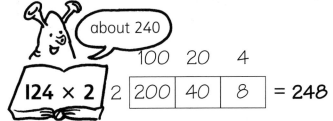 about 240

124 × 2   2 | 200 | 40 | 8 | = 248

100   20   4

about

142 × 5   [| |] =

about

132 × 2   100   30   2   [| |] =

about

234 × 5   [| |] =

about

 153 × 2   [| |] =

about

243 × 6   [| |] =

about

123 × 3   [| |] =

about

325 × 6   [| |] =

about

231 × 3   [| |] =

about

423 × 7   [| |] =

about

203 × 3   [| |] =

about

532 × 8   [| |] =

about

210 × 4   [| |] =

about

623 × 9   [| |] =

Masterpieces Ginn & Company 1999. Copying permitted for purchasing school only. This material is not copyright free.

Name _____ Date _____

TU ÷ U

1 32 sweets ÷ 2 = ☐ each

24 sweets ÷ 2 = ☐ each   30 sweets ÷ 2 = ☐ each

36 sweets ÷ 2 = ☐ each   42 sweets ÷ 2 = ☐ each

35 sweets ÷ 5 = ☐ each   45 sweets ÷ 5 = ☐ each

75 sweets ÷ 5 = ☐ each   95 sweets ÷ 5 = ☐ each

2 Write the questions that give these answers.

☐ ÷ 2 = 10   ☐ ÷ 2 = 9   ☐ ÷ 2 = 11

☐ ÷ 5 = 10   ☐ ÷ 5 = 6   ☐ ÷ 5 = 8

3 Write some more questions like these.

Name _____ Date _____

TU ÷ U

1 Help Jason to share the coloured pencils with his group. How many will each person get?

$24 \div 3 =$ ⬡ $25 \div 5 =$ ⬡ $24 \div 4 =$ ⬡

$30 \div 2 =$ ⬡ $48 \div 3 =$ ⬡ $40 \div 2 =$ ⬡

$48 \div 4 =$ ⬡ $39 \div 3 =$ ⬡ $36 \div 4 =$ ⬡

$54 \div 6 =$ ⬡ $66 \div 6 =$ ⬡ $100 \div 4 =$ ⬡

2 Write as many division questions as you can to give the answer 20.

$40 \div 2$

$(200 \div 2) \div 5$

20

Name _____ Date _____

TU ÷ U

1 Join up the questions to the answers.

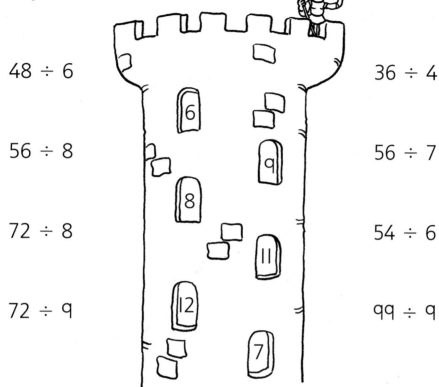

48 ÷ 6   36 ÷ 4

56 ÷ 8   56 ÷ 7

72 ÷ 8   54 ÷ 6

72 ÷ 9   99 ÷ 9

2 Write as many division questions as you can which give the answer 18.

18   36 ÷ 2

3 Write questions that give these answers.

☐ ÷ ☐ = 11   ☐ ÷ ☐ = 5   ☐ ÷ ☐ = 8

4 Make up some more questions like these.

Name _____ Date _____

Remainders as whole numbers

Mrs Green the grocer is putting fruit in bags.

1  If she puts these apples in bags of 2 each, how many will be left over? [ ]
If she puts them in bags of 5 each, how many will be left over? [ ]

2 17 bananas in bags of 2 each. How many left over? [ ]
17 bananas in bags of 5 each. How many left over? [ ]

3 27 oranges in bags of 2 each. How many left over? [ ]
27 oranges in bags of 5 each. How many left over? [ ]

4 34 pears in bags of 2 each. How many left over? [ ]
34 pears in bags of 5 each. How many left over? [ ]

5 29 plums in bags of 2. How many bags? [ ]
How many left over? [ ]

29 plums in bags of 5. How many bags? [ ]
How many left over? [ ]

6 Make up your own bags of fruit. How many bags will you need? How many will be left over? [ ]

Name _____ Date _____

Remainders: rounding up or down

John and Jo go to the supermarket.

1 Jo buys 27 tomatoes. A bag holds 2 tomatoes.
How many bags will she need? ☐

2 John buys 32 potatoes. A bag holds 5 potatoes.
How many bags will he need? ☐

3 Jo buys 44 potatoes.
How many bags will she need? ☐

4  John buys 32 carrots. A bag holds 3 carrots.
How many bags will he need? ☐

5 Jo buys 47 carrots.
How many bags will she need? ☐

6 John has £43. T shirts costs £4 each.
How many T shirts could he buy? ☐

7 Jo has £66. Footballs costs £4.
How many footballs could she buy? ☐

8 Jo buys 53 eggs. An eggbox holds 6 eggs.
How many boxes could she fill? ☐

9 John buys 68 eggs. How many boxes could he fill? ☐

Name _____ Date _____

Remainders as decimals

1 Write the answers in the baskets under the balloons.

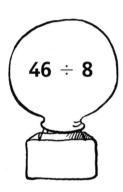

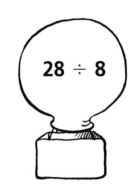

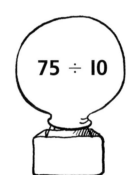

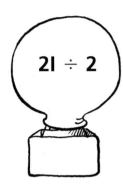

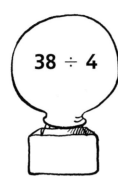

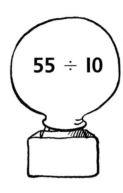

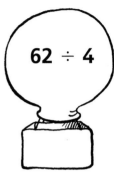

2 4 friends go to the shops. They all spend the same amount.

If they spend a total of £22, how much does each spend?	If they spend a total of £26, how much does each spend?
If they spend a total of £41, how much does each spend?	If they spend a total of £55, how much does each spend?

3 The answer is 7.5. How many division questions can you write?

Masterpieces Ginn & Company 1999. Copying permitted for purchasing school only. This material is not copyright free.

Name _____ Date _____

Diagnostic assessment

1 Circle the correct answer to each question.

$21 \times 3 =$ 24   63   127

$11 \times 13 =$ 103   3   143

2 Circle any numbers that are in the 10× table.

57   23   30   50   100   43

3 Circle any numbers that are in the 100× table.

530   200   705   800   100   10

A
Sheets

4 Circle the correct answer to each question.

$21 \times 9 =$ 219   189   30

$11 \times 27 =$ 38   1127   297

5 Circle any numbers that are exactly divisible by 2.

57   23   30   16   19   44

6 Circle any numbers that are exactly divisible by 5.

65   20   75   54   68   40

B
Sheets

7 Circle the correct answer to each question.

$104 \times 6 =$ 624   110   1046

$11 \times 70 =$ 1170   770   81

8 Circle any numbers that are exactly divisible by 3.

24   43   30   54   35   72

9 Circle any numbers that are exactly divisible by 4.

16   80   45   54   64   94

C
Sheets

Name _____ Date _____

Checking with the inverse operation

1 Do each question and check your answer in the way shown.

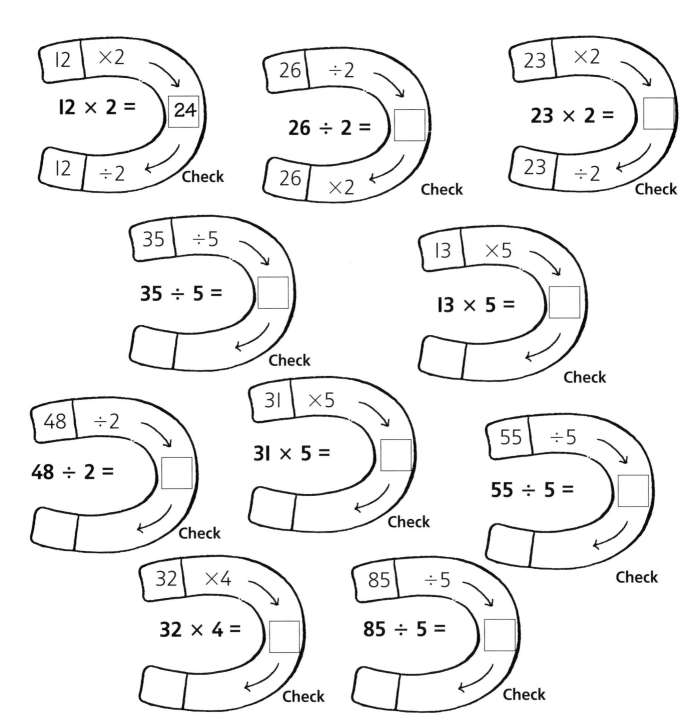

2 Answer these questions and check them in the same way.

$14 \times 2 =$ $35 \times 4 =$ $95 \div 5 =$ $450 \div 10 =$

Name _____ Date _____

Checking with the inverse operation

1 Do each question and check your answer in the way shown.

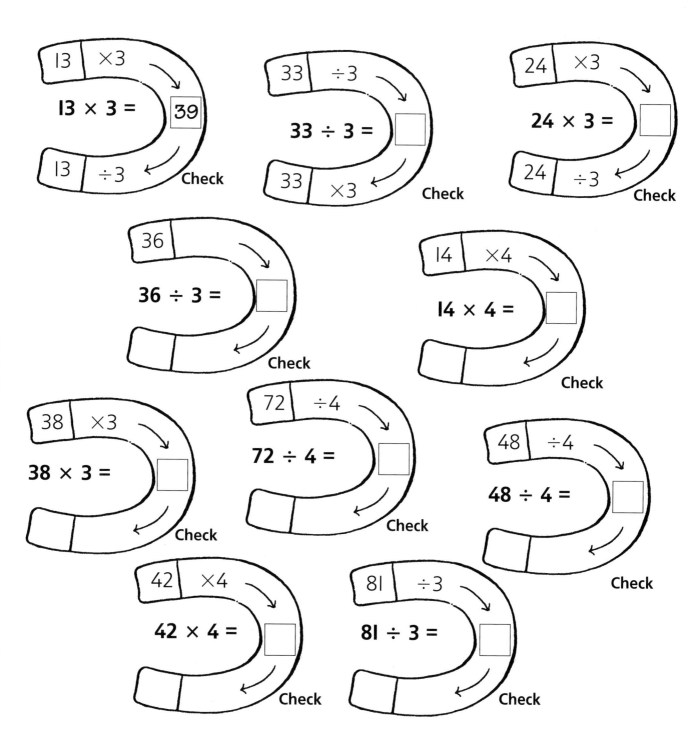

13 ×3

13 × 3 = 39

13 ÷3 Check

33 ÷3

33 ÷ 3 = ☐

33 ×3 Check

24 ×3

24 × 3 = ☐

24 ÷3 Check

36

36 ÷ 3 = ☐

Check

14 ×4

14 × 4 = ☐

Check

38 ×3

38 × 3 = ☐

Check

72 ÷4

72 ÷ 4 = ☐

Check

48 ÷4

48 ÷ 4 = ☐

Check

42 ×4

42 × 4 = ☐

Check

81 ÷3

81 ÷ 3 = ☐

Check

2 Answer these questions and check them in the same way.

24 × 2 =   46 × 6 =   51 ÷ 3 =   860 ÷ 10 =

Name _____   Date _____

Checking with the inverse operation

1 Do each question and check your answer in the way shown.

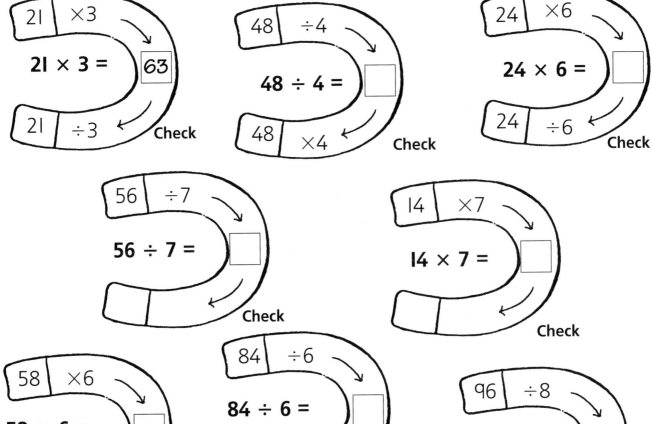

| 21 | ×3 |
| 21 × 3 = | 63 |
| 21 | ÷3 | Check

| 48 | ÷4 |
| 48 ÷ 4 = | |
| 48 | ×4 | Check

| 24 | ×6 |
| 24 × 6 = | |
| 24 | ÷6 | Check

| 56 | ÷7 |
| 56 ÷ 7 = | |
| | | Check

| 14 | ×7 |
| 14 × 7 = | |
| | | Check

| 58 | ×6 |
| 58 × 6 = | |
| | | Check

| 84 | ÷6 |
| 84 ÷ 6 = | |
| | | Check

| 96 | ÷8 |
| 96 ÷ 8 = | |
| | | Check

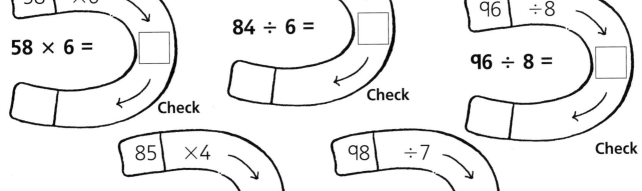

| 85 | ×4 |
| 85 × 4 = | |
| | | Check

| 98 | ÷7 |
| 98 ÷ 7 = | |
| | | Check

2 Answer these questions and check them in the same way.

$63 \times 7 =$ $78 \times 9 =$ $96 \div 6 =$ $930 \div 10 =$

Name _____ Date _____

Repeating multiplication in a different order

Draw a loop to show which multiplication you work out first.
Show another way. Circle the way you think is easiest.

Ist way	**2nd way**
$2 \times 10 \times 5 =$ ⌣ $\boxed{100}$	$2 \times 10 \times 5 =$ ⌣ $\boxed{100}$

1 $2 \times 3 \times 5 = \boxed{}$ $\qquad$ $2 \times 3 \times 5 = \boxed{}$

2 $2 \times 4 \times 5 = \boxed{}$ $\qquad$ $2 \times 4 \times 5 = \boxed{}$

3 $10 \times 4 \times 5 = \boxed{}$ $\qquad$ $10 \times 4 \times 5 = \boxed{}$

4 $2 \times 4 \times 10 = \boxed{}$ $\qquad$ $2 \times 4 \times 10 = \boxed{}$

5 $3 \times 10 \times 5 = \boxed{}$ $\qquad$ $3 \times 10 \times 5 = \boxed{}$

6 $10 \times 3 \times 4 = \boxed{}$ $\qquad$ $10 \times 3 \times 4 = \boxed{}$

7 $3 \times 4 \times 5 = \boxed{}$ $\qquad$ $3 \times 4 \times 5 = \boxed{}$

8 $4 \times 6 \times 10 = \boxed{}$ $\qquad$ $4 \times 6 \times 10 = \boxed{}$

9 $2 \times 4 \times 6 = \boxed{}$ $\qquad$ $2 \times 4 \times 6 = \boxed{}$

10 $10 \times 6 \times 5 = \boxed{}$ $\qquad$ $10 \times 6 \times 5 = \boxed{}$

Name _____ Date _____

Repeating multiplication in a different order

Draw a loop to show which multiplication you work out first.
Show another way. Circle the way you think is easiest.

	1st way	**2nd way**
	$3 \times 4 \times 5 =$ 60	$3 \times 4 \times 5 =$ 60
1	$4 \times 5 \times 10 =$	$4 \times 5 \times 10 =$
2	$10 \times 6 \times 5 =$	$10 \times 6 \times 5 =$
3	$2 \times 6 \times 4 =$	$2 \times 6 \times 4 =$
4	$5 \times 6 \times 4 =$	$5 \times 6 \times 4 =$
5	$2 \times 5 \times 6 =$	$2 \times 5 \times 6 =$
6	$10 \times 5 \times 7 =$	$10 \times 5 \times 7 =$
7	$3 \times 7 \times 10 =$	$3 \times 7 \times 10 =$
8	$5 \times 4 \times 8 =$	$5 \times 4 \times 8 =$
9	$3 \times 7 \times 5 =$	$3 \times 7 \times 5 =$
10	$2 \times 7 \times 4 =$	$2 \times 7 \times 4 =$

Masterpieces Ginn & Company 1999. Copying permitted for purchasing school only. This material is not copyright free.

Name _____ Date _____

Repeating multiplication in a different order

Draw a loop to show which multiplication you work out first. Show another way on the next question. Circle the way you think is easiest.

	1st way	**2nd way**
	$6 \times 7 \times 2 =$ 84	$6 \times 7 \times 2 =$ 84
1	$5 \times 6 \times 8 =$ ☐	$5 \times 6 \times 8 =$ ☐
2	$3 \times 7 \times 5 =$ ☐	$3 \times 7 \times 5 =$ ☐
3	$2 \times 6 \times 8 =$ ☐	$2 \times 6 \times 8 =$ ☐
4	$2 \times 9 \times 4 =$ ☐	$2 \times 9 \times 4 =$ ☐
5	$6 \times 5 \times 7 =$ ☐	$6 \times 5 \times 7 =$ ☐
6	$2 \times 8 \times 9 =$ ☐	$2 \times 8 \times 9 =$ ☐
7	$3 \times 7 \times 8 =$ ☐	$3 \times 7 \times 8 =$ ☐
8	$4 \times 6 \times 9 =$ ☐	$4 \times 6 \times 9 =$ ☐
9	$7 \times 4 \times 6 =$ ☐	$7 \times 4 \times 6 =$ ☐
10	$9 \times 3 \times 8 =$ ☐	$9 \times 3 \times 8 =$ ☐

Checking by approximating
(rounding to the nearest 10)

This is Deepa's homework.
Write an **approximate** answer for each question to help her.

Deepa

1 $11 \times 12 =$

2 $11 \times 15 =$

3 $11 \times 20 =$

4 $11 \times 21 =$

5 $11 \times 30 =$

6 $11 \times 40 =$

7 $11 \times 45 =$

8 $11 \times 50 =$

1 $12 \times 2 =$

2 $19 \times 2 =$

3 $12 \times 5 =$

4 $19 \times 5 =$

5 $21 \times 3 =$

6 $19 \times 4 =$

Name _____ Date _____

Checking by approximating
(rounding to the nearest 10 or 100)

This is David's homework.
Write an **approximate** answer for each question to help him.

David

1 11 × 18 =

2 11 × 22 =

3 9 × 20 =

4 9 × 21 =

1 28 × 2 =

2 19 × 5 =

3 22 × 3 =

4 29 × 3 =

5 38 × 4 =

6 52 × 4 =

1 203 × 5 =

2 199 × 3

3 302 × 3 =

4 298 × 4 =

Name _____ Date _____

Checking by approximating
(rounding to the nearest 10 or 100)

1 Chris went on holiday to a hotel. It had 4 floors and 32 windows on each floor. About how many windows were there? ☐

2 About how many windows are in these hotels?

Orion Hotel	5 floors and 48 windows on each floor	☐
Star Hotel	6 floors and 52 windows on each floor	☐
Sun Hotel	6 floors and 102 windows on each floor	☐
Beach Hotel	11 floors and 215 windows on each floor	☐
Cliff Hotel	9 floors and 195 windows on each floor	☐

3 Help the window cleaner by finding about how many windows there are in these hotels.

11 floors and 130 windows ☐	9 floors and 142 windows ☐
8 floors and 40 windows ☐	11 floors and 65 windows ☐
29 floors and 15 windows ☐	32 floors and 21 windows ☐
12 floors and 107 windows ☐	19 floors and 33 windows ☐

Checking with an equivalent calculation

1 Find 2 other ways to answer these questions.

$21 \times 2 = \boxed{}$ | $21 + 21 = \boxed{}$ | $20 \times 2 + 1 \times 2 = \boxed{}$

$25 \times 2 = \boxed{}$ | $\boxed{} + \boxed{} = \boxed{}$ | $\boxed{} \times \boxed{} + \boxed{} \times \boxed{} = \boxed{}$

$36 \times 2 = \boxed{}$ | $\boxed{} + \boxed{} = \boxed{}$ | $\boxed{} \times \boxed{} + \boxed{} \times \boxed{} = \boxed{}$

$39 \times 2 = \boxed{}$ | $\boxed{} + \boxed{} = \boxed{}$ | $\boxed{} \times \boxed{} + \boxed{} \times \boxed{} = \boxed{}$

$41 \times 3 = \boxed{}$ | $\boxed{} + \boxed{} + \boxed{} = \boxed{}$ | $\boxed{} \times \boxed{} + \boxed{} \times \boxed{} = \boxed{}$

$43 \times 3 = \boxed{}$ | $\boxed{} + \boxed{} + \boxed{} = \boxed{}$ | $\boxed{} \times \boxed{} + \boxed{} \times \boxed{} = \boxed{}$

2 Choose your own questions for these trains.

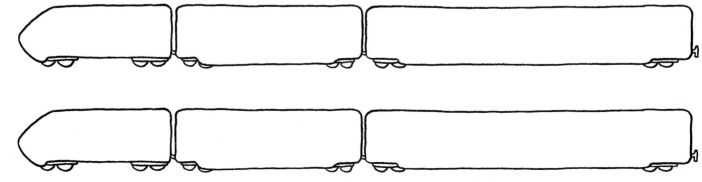

Name _____ Date _____

Checking with an equivalent calculation

1 Find 2 other ways to answer these questions.

$32 \times 3 = \boxed{}$ $32 + 32 + 32 = \boxed{}$ $30 \times 3 + 2 \times 3 = \boxed{}$

$35 \times 3 = \boxed{}$ $\boxed{} + \boxed{} + \boxed{} = \boxed{}$ $\boxed{} \times \boxed{} + \boxed{} \times \boxed{} = \boxed{}$

$46 \times 3 = \boxed{}$ $\boxed{} + \boxed{} + \boxed{} = \boxed{}$ $\boxed{} \times \boxed{} + \boxed{} \times \boxed{} = \boxed{}$

$38 \times 3 = \boxed{}$ $\boxed{} + \boxed{} + \boxed{} = \boxed{}$ $\boxed{} \times \boxed{} + \boxed{} \times \boxed{} = \boxed{}$

$52 \times 3 = \boxed{}$ $\boxed{} + \boxed{} + \boxed{} = \boxed{}$ $\boxed{} \times \boxed{} + \boxed{} \times \boxed{} = \boxed{}$

$49 \times 3 = \boxed{}$ $\boxed{} + \boxed{} + \boxed{} = \boxed{}$ $\boxed{} \times \boxed{} + \boxed{} \times \boxed{} = \boxed{}$

2 Write your own questions.

Masterpieces Ginn & Company 1999.

Name _____ Date _____

Checking with an equivalent calculation

1 Check Jimmy's homework by doing the questions in a different way.
Tick the ones he got right.

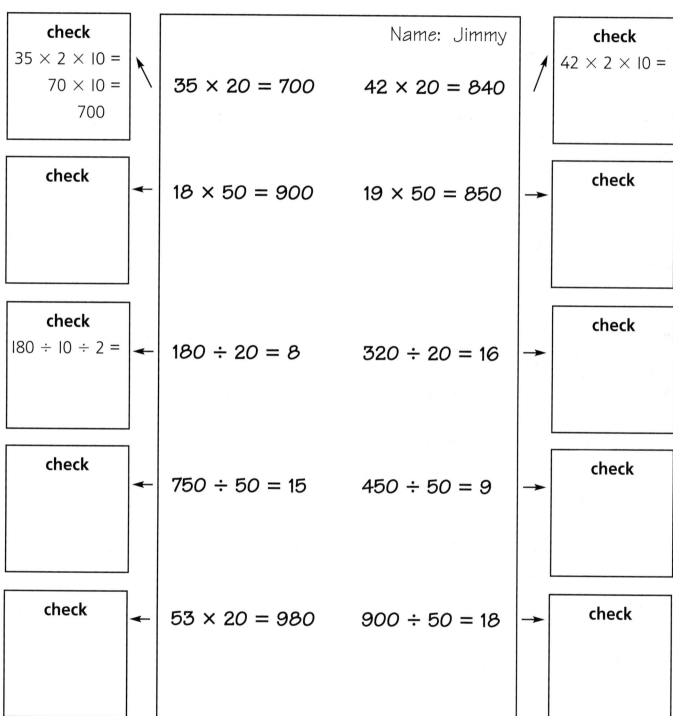

check
35 × 2 × 10 =
70 × 10 =
700

Name: Jimmy

check
42 × 2 × 10 =

35 × 20 = 700   42 × 20 = 840

check

18 × 50 = 900   19 × 50 = 850

check

check
180 ÷ 10 ÷ 2 =

180 ÷ 20 = 8   320 ÷ 20 = 16

check

check

750 ÷ 50 = 15   450 ÷ 50 = 9

check

check

53 × 20 = 980   900 ÷ 50 = 18

check

2 How could you do these in another way?

31 × 40 =   640 ÷ 40 =

Name _____ Date _____

Using tests of divisibility by 10 and 100

1 Write some numbers from the
   10 times table.

2 Write some numbers from the
   100 times table.

What do you notice about these numbers? ....

....

3 Colour green the numbers in the **10×** table.

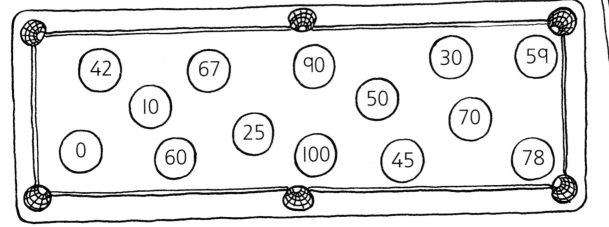

4 Colour red the numbers in the **100×** table.

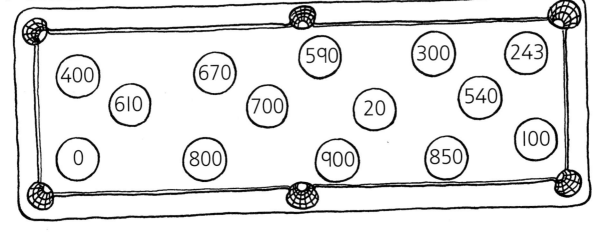

 A *Masterpieces:* **Multiplication and Division** CHECKING RESULTS   YEARS 3/4

Name _____   Date _____

Using tests of divisibility by 2 and 5

1	2	3	4	5	6	7	8	9	10
11	12	13	14	15	16	17	18	19	20
21	22	23	24	25	26	27	28	29	30
31	32	33	34	35	36	37	38	39	40
41	42	43	44	45	46	47	48	49	50
51	52	53	54	55	56	57	58	59	60
61	62	63	64	65	66	67	68	69	70
71	72	73	74	75	76	77	78	79	80
81	82	83	84	85	86	87	88	89	90
91	92	93	94	95	96	97	98	99	100

1 On the grid colour all the **even** numbers in yellow.
How can you recognise these numbers?

....

2 Colour yellow the numbers that are exactly **divisible by 2**.

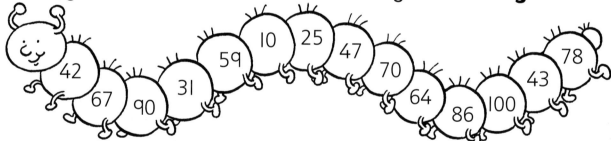

3 Colour in red the numbers that are exactly **divisible by 5**.

How can you recognise these numbers?

....

Name _____ Date _____

Using tests of divisibility by 3 and 4

1 Complete the 3 times table in the **first** snake.

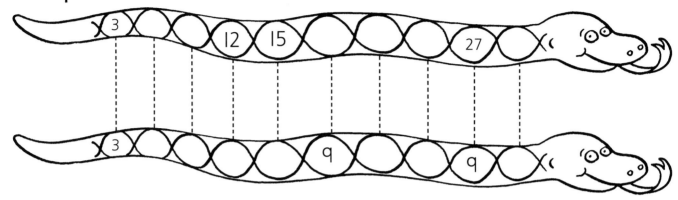

To make the numbers in the **second** snake, add the digits of the
number above, so 15 → 1 + 5 = 6
What do you notice about the numbers in the second snake?

....

Write some more numbers that are exactly **divisible by 3**.

2

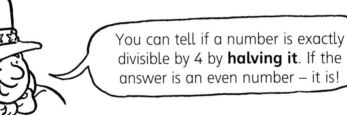

You can tell if a number is exactly
divisible by 4 by **halving it**. If the
answer is an even number – it is!

Circle the numbers that are exactly **divisible by 4**.

28	16	18	22	15
24	50	46	88	79
54	62	68	91	100

Write some more numbers that are exactly divisible by 4.

Answers

Page 4 – Diagnostic assessment

1 4	12	25
40	50	100

2 14	30	36
6	8	10

3 9	24	27
16	24	32

4 32	48	62
7	12	21

5 36	42	49
64	72	81

6 42	56	74
9	21	39

Page 5

4 5	5	4	4
3	9	8	10
14	10	6	6

Page 6

3 5	6	10	6
7	9	8	9

Page 7

3 18	49	45	42
0	5	8	7
9	7	81	0
72	7	8	9

Page 8

1	15
10	20
30	25
35	40
45	50

Page 9

1 100	130
140	160
180	210
230	250
115	135
145	165
175	205
215	245

Page 10

1	150
200	300
400	600
700	900
1400	750
850	1050
1450	1750
1500	1900

Page 12

1 64
46
68
50
76
82
52
66

2 8	12	18	19	22
20	25	28	32	38

Page 13

1 52
78
86
90
94
98
76
58

2 12	17	18	21	19
23	25	34	38	42

Page 14

1	20
30	40
50	60
70	80
90	100

2 55→110, 60→120, 65→130, 70→140, 75→150
80→160, 85→170, 90→180, 95→190, 100→200

Page 17 – Diagnostic assessment

1 10 60

2 132 154 275

3 230 16 34

4 12 28

5 108 135 243

6 3100 80 13

7 240 240
48 90

8 143 126 150

9 26000 8

Page 18

1 20 25 30 35 40 45 50
40 50 60 70 80 90 100

2 40 80
6 12 20 40
12 24 50 100
16 32 70 140

3 30 15
40 20 50 25
60 30 70 35
80 40 90 45

Page 19

1 21 42
18 36 27 54
18 36 28 56
32 64 90 180

2 40 80 60 120
36 72 100 200
60 120 160 320

3 30 15
40 20 50 25
60 30 70 35
80 40 90 45

4 300 150 160 80
120 60 150 75

Page 20

1 160
90 180 120 240
72 144 240 480
72 144 180 360

2 150
500 250 400 200
170 85 250 125
360 180 420 210

3 50 60 70
100 120 140
200 240 280
400 480 560
800 960 1120

Page 21

1 165
176
220
275
330

2 187 231 264
209
396
440
495

Page 22

1 153
234
270
315

2 9×34=306   9×45=405
9×32=288   9×53=477
9×65=585   9×38=342
9×50=450   9×42=378

Page 23

1 24 30 36 42
48 54 66 72

2 36 45 54 63
72 81 99 108

Page 24

1 30
60 80
60 44
95 90

Page 25

1 78
135 144

2 190 172
270 201

Page 26

I	100	20	3
	100	30	4
	100	40	5
	100	50	6
	100	30	0
	100	0	3
	100	80	1

Page 27

I		24
	350	32
	460	40
	580	53
	730	85
	920	97

2	45	1240
	56	2360
	61	3570
	70	7770
	98	6600
	100	9090

Page 28

I	600	2	6
	3200		9
	5800		12
	6400		23
	19800		360

3		4500		5
		600		53
	99		7000	
		6200		47
	58		4500	
		8300		3

Page 29

I	7000	2	4
	62000		8
	98000		41
	64000		67

3	4000	23000
	38000	72000
	6	8
	15	36

4	31000
	11000
	66000
	40000

Page 30 – Diagnostic assessment

1 20	30	50	80
2 46	105	88	
8	5	7r1	
3 40	50	90	100
4 300	500	400	700
5 102	172	180	
7	9r2	7r3	
6 120		360	
100		400	
7 268	572	1730	
8	8r4	9r3	

Page 31

1 30	40	40
40	50	70
80	90	100

Page 32

1 30	150	200	1000
40	120	300	600
20	100	300	1500
20	100	400	800
20	40	400	1200
20	40	500	2000
30	60	600	1800
30	90	600	1200

Page 33

1

100×4 larger

300×6 larger

300×8 larger

300×7 smaller

600×9 smaller

Page 34

1 42	46
44	39
55	60
88	69

Page 35

1

64	
128	96

2 270

108	216
162	540

3 185

74	148
370	111

4 395

158	316
790	237

Page 36

1

	710
264	1170
306	1458
369	1950
693	2961
609	4256
840	5607

Page 37

1 16

12	15
18	21
7	9
15	19

2 20	18	22
50	30	40

Page 38

1 8	5	6
15	16	20
12	13	9
9	11	25

Page 39

1 8	9
7	8
9	9
8	11

Page 40

1 1, 3	**4** 0, 4
2 1, 2	**5** 14, 1
	5, 4
3 1, 2	

Page 41

1 14	**6** 10
2 7	**7** 16
3 9	**8** 8
4 11	**9** 11
5 16	

Page 42

1 10.5	9.5	5.5	15.5
5.75	3.5	7.5	16.5

2 £5.50	£6.50
£10.25	£13.75

Page 43 – Diagnostic assessment

1 63
143

2 30   50   100

3 200   800   100

4 189
297

5 30   16   44

6 65   20   75   40

7 624
770

8 24   30   54   72

9 16   80   64

Page 44

1 13   46
7   65
24   155   11
128   17

2 28   140   19   45

Page 45

1   11   72
12   56
114   18   12
168   27

2 48   276   17   86

Page 46

1   12   144
8   98
348   14   12
340   14

2 441   702   16   93

Page 47

1 30   2 40   3 200   4 80   5 150

6 120   7 60   8 240   9 48   10 300

Page 48

1 200   2 300   3 48   4 120   5 60

6 350   7 210   8 160   9 105   10 56

Page 49

1 240   2 105   3 96   4 72   5 210

6 144   7 168   8 216   9 168   10 216

Page 50

1 120   2 150
3 200   4 210
5 300   6 400
7 450   8 500

1 20   2 40
3 50   4 100
5 60   6 80

Page 51

1 180   2 220
3 200   4 210

1 60   2 100
3 60   4 90
5 160   6 200

1 1000   2 600
3 900   4 1200

Page 52

1 120

2 250
300
600
2150
1950

3 1300   1420
400   650
450   630 or 640
1200   660

Page 53

1 42
50   25+25   20×2 + 5×2
72   36+36   30×2 + 6×2
78   39+39   30×2 + 9×2
123   41+41+41   40×3 + 1×3
129   43+43+43   40×3 + 3×3

Page 54

1 96

105	35+35+35	30×3 + 5×3
138	46+46+46	40×3 + 6×3
114	38+38+38	30×3 + 8×3
156	52+52+52	50×3 + 2×3
147	49+49+49	40×3 + 9×3

Page 55

700 ✓	840 ✓
900 ✓	16 ✓
15 ✓	9 ✓
	18 ✓

Page 56

3 90 30 10 50 70 0 60 100

4 400 300 700 0 800 900 100

Page 57

3 42 90 10 70 64 86 100 78

4 45 90 10 25 70 100 75

Page 58

1 3 6 9 12 15 18 21 24 27 30
   3 6 9 3 6 9 3 6 9 3

2 28 16 24 88 68 100